IT'S NOT FAIR!

Jokes compiled by Beth Goodman

Pictures by B.K. Taylor

SCHOLASTIC INC.

New York   Toronto   London   Auckland   Sydney

ISBN 0-590-41242-6

Copyright © 1988 by Scholastic Books, Inc.
All rights reserved. Published by Scholastic Inc.

12 11 10 9 8 7 6 5 4 3 2 1   8 9/8 0 1 2 3/9

Printed in the U.S.A.   11

First Scholastic printing, January 1988

It's Not Fair!
The teacher never calls on you when
you do know the answers — only when
you don't!

It's Not Fair!
Liver, lima beans, and cottage cheese
are good for you, and bubble gum is bad
for you!

It's Not Fair!
You're all set to see a great movie — and then a seven-foot giant sits in front of you!

It's Not Fair!
As soon as you start finger painting,
you get an itchy nose!

It's Not Fair!
You spend an hour making your bed, and
then your dog jumps on it!

It's Not Fair!
You always get strikes in baseball
but never in bowling!

It's Not Fair!
You lick the envelope shut and
forget to put the letter in!

It's Not Fair!
You get a new record, and your brother
uses it as a Frisbee!

It's Not Fair!
You wear your raincoat, hat, and boots to school, and it doesn't even rain a drop!

It's Not Fair!
It's your birthday, and someone else
blows out your candles!

It's Not Fair!
The pet kitten you got for your birthday
likes to sleep on your sister's bed!

It's Not Fair!
When you take a break from your
homework, your mom tells you to clean up
your room!

It's Not Fair!
On the first day of vacation you get sick!

It's Not Fair!
Every time you eat macaroni and cheese,
the noodles slip off your fork!

It's Not Fair!
You spend a dollar on baseball cards
and you get all doubles!

It's Not Fair!
You have to go to bed when you're
not tired and you have to get up when
you are tired!

It's Not Fair!
You get a new puzzle and a piece
is missing!

It's Not Fair!
Your gym teacher puts you on one team
and your best friend on another!

It's Not Fair!
After you lose your two front teeth,
you get corn on the cob for dinner!

It's Not Fair!
You want to be Cinderella in the school play but you get the part of the wicked stepmother!

It's Not Fair!
Your mother yells every time your lizard
gets loose!

It's Not Fair!
You share a room with your sister, and
she snores!

It's Not Fair!
You want to buy a hot lunch at school, and the only thing hot is the milk!

It's Not Fair!
It's your birthday and you get the
smallest piece of cake!

It's Not Fair!
Your name is spelled wrong
in the school yearbook!

It's Not Fair!
Your favorite TV show changes its time
from 8:00 to 9:00, and that's when
you have to go to bed!

It's Not Fair!
You move into a new house, and
your sister gets the bigger bedroom!

It's Not Fair!
You are in the middle of a good dream,
and your mom wakes you up for school!

It's Not Fair!
You run for class president but you get
elected class clown!